# Travis – 12 Mem

**TAB**
EDITION

**Sony Music Publishing**

# Guitar Tablature Explained

Guitar music can be notated in three different ways: on a musical stave, in tablature, and in rhythm slashes.

**RHYTHM SLASHES** are written above the stave. Strum chords in the rhythm indicated. Round noteheads indicate single notes.

**THE MUSICAL STAVE** shows pitches and rhythms and is divided by lines into bars. Pitches are named after the first seven letters of the alphabet.

**TABLATURE** graphically represents the guitar fingerboard. Each horizontal line represents a string, and each number represents a fret.

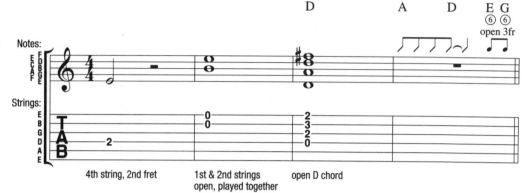

4th string, 2nd fret    1st & 2nd strings open, played together    open D chord

# Definitions For Special Guitar Notation

**SEMI-TONE BEND:** Strike the note and bend up a semi-tone (1/2 step).

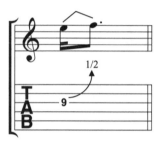

**WHOLE-TONE BEND:** Strike the note and bend up a whole-tone (whole step).

**GRACE NOTE BEND:** Strike the note and bend as indicated. Play the first note as quickly as possible.

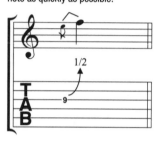

**QUARTER-TONE BEND:** Strike the note and bend up a 1/4 step.

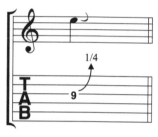

**BEND & RELEASE:** Strike the note and bend up as indicated, then release back to the original note.

**COMPOUND BEND & RELEASE:** Strike the note and bend up and down in the rhythm indicated.

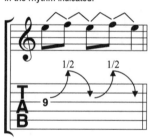

**PRE-BEND:** Bend the note as indicated, then strike it.

**PRE-BEND & RELEASE:** Bend the note as indicated. Strike it and release the note back to the original pitch.

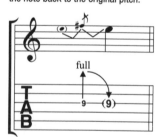

**UNISON BEND:** Strike the two notes simultaneously and bend the lower note up to the pitch of the higher.

**BEND & RESTRIKE:** Strike the note and bend as indicated then restrike the string where the symbol occurs.

**BEND, HOLD AND RELEASE:** Same as bend and release but hold the bend for the duration of the tie.

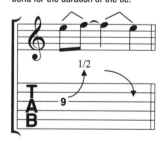

**BEND AND TAP:** Bend the note as indicated and tap the higher fret while still holding the bend.

**VIBRATO:** The string is vibrated by rapidly bending and releasing the note with the fretting hand.

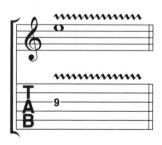

**HAMMER-ON:** Strike the first note with one finger, then sound the second note (on the same string) with another finger by fretting it without picking.

**PULL-OFF:** Place both fingers on the notes to be sounded, strike the first note and without picking, pull the finger off to sound the second note.

**LEGATO SLIDE (GLISS):** Strike the first note and then slide the same fret-hand finger up or down to the second note. The second note is not struck.

**NOTE:** The speed of any bend is indicated by the music notation and tempo.

**SHIFT SLIDE (GLISS & RESTRIKE):** Same as legato slide, except the second note is struck.

**TRILL:** Very rapidly alternate between the notes indicated by continuously hammering on and pulling off.

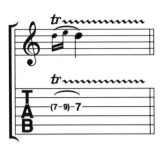

**TAPPING:** Hammer ("tap") the fret indicated with the pick-hand index or middle finger and pull off to the note fretted by the fret hand.

**PICK SCRAPE:** The edge of the pick is rubbed down (or up) the string, producing a scratchy sound.

**MUFFLED STRINGS:** A percussive sound is produced by laying the fret hand across the string(s) without depressing, and striking them with the pick hand.

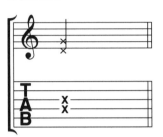

**NATURAL HARMONIC:** Strike the note while the fret-hand lightly touches the string directly over the fret indicated.

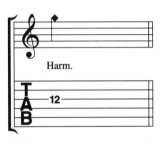

**PINCH HARMONIC:** The note is fretted normally and a harmonic is produced by adding the edge of the thumb or the tip of the index finger of the pick hand to the normal pick attack.

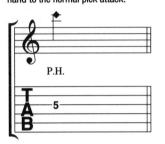

**HARP HARMONIC:** The note is fretted normally and a harmonic is produced by gently resting the pick hand's index finger directly above the indicated fret (in brackets) while plucking the appropriate string.

**PALM MUTING:** The note is partially muted by the pick hand lightly touching the string(s) just before the bridge.

**RAKE:** Drag the pick across the strings indicated with a single motion.

**TREMOLO PICKING:** The note is picked as rapidly and continuously as possible.

**ARPEGGIATE:** Play the notes of the chord indicated by quickly rolling them from bottom to top.

**SWEEP PICKING:** Rhythmic downstroke and/or upstroke motion across the strings.

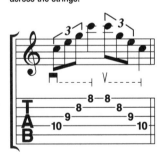

**VIBRATO DIVE BAR AND RETURN:** The pitch of the note or chord is dropped a specific number of steps (in rhythm) then returned to the original pitch.

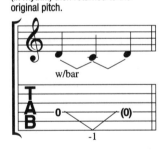

**VIBRATO BAR SCOOP:** Depress the bar just before striking the note, then quickly release the bar.

**VIBRATO BAR DIP:** Strike the note and then immediately drop a specific number of steps, then release back to the original pitch.

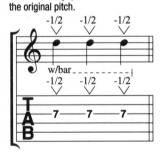

# Additional Musical Definitions

| | | |
|---|---|---|
|  | (accent) | • Accentuate note (play it louder). |
|  | (accent) | • Accentuate note with great intensity. |
|  | (staccato) | • Shorten time value of note. |
|  | | • Downstroke |
| V | | • Upstroke |

**D.%. al Coda**

• Go back to the sign (%), then play until the bar marked *To Coda* ⊕ then skip to the section marked ⊕ *Coda*.

**D.C. al Fine**

• Go back to the beginning of the song and play until the bar marked *Fine*.

tacet

• Instrument is silent (drops out).

• Repeat bars between signs.

• When a repeated section has different endings, play the first ending only the first time and the second ending only the second time.

**NOTE:** Tablature numbers in brackets mean:
1. The note is sustained, but a new articulation (such as hammer on or slide) begins.
2. A note may be fretted but not necessarily played.

Exclusive distributors:
**Music Sales Limited**
Distribution Centre, Newmarket Road,
Bury St Edmunds, Suffolk IP33 3YB, England.
**Music Sales Pty Limited**
120 Rothschild Avenue, Rosebery, NSW 2018, Australia.

Order No. AM979341
ISBN 1-84449-371-7
This book © Copyright 2003 by Sony Music Publishing.

Unauthorised reproduction of any part of this publication by
any means including photocopying is an infringement of copyright.

Music arrangements by Matt Cowe.
Music processed by Paul Ewers Music Design.

Printed in the United Kingdom

www.musicsales.com

**Your Guarantee of Quality:**

As publishers, we strive to produce every book
to the highest commercial standards.

While endeavouring to retain the original running order of the
recorded album, the book has been carefully designed to minimise
awkward page turns and to make playing from it a real pleasure.

Particular care has been given to specifying
acid-free, neutral-sized paper made from pulps which
have not been elemental chlorine bleached.

This pulp is from farmed sustainable forests and
was produced with special regard for the environment.

Throughout, the printing and binding have been
planned to ensure a sturdy, attractive publication
which should give years of enjoyment.

If your copy fails to meet our high standards,
please inform us and we will gladly replace it.

# Re-Offender

Lyrics & Music by Fran Healy

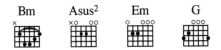

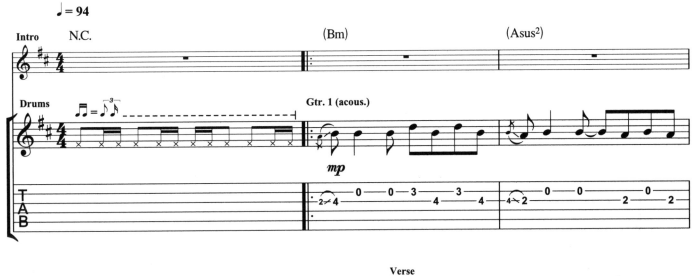

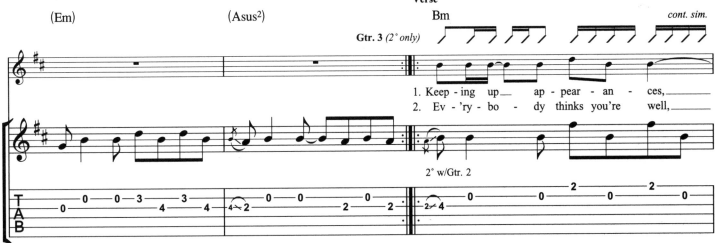

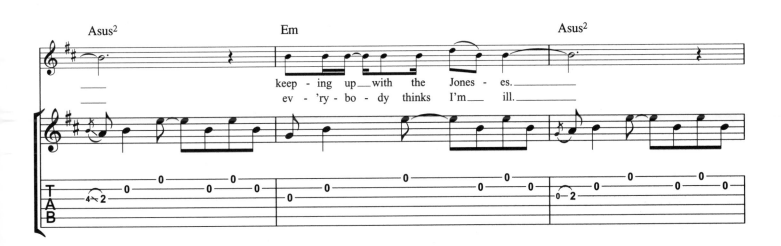

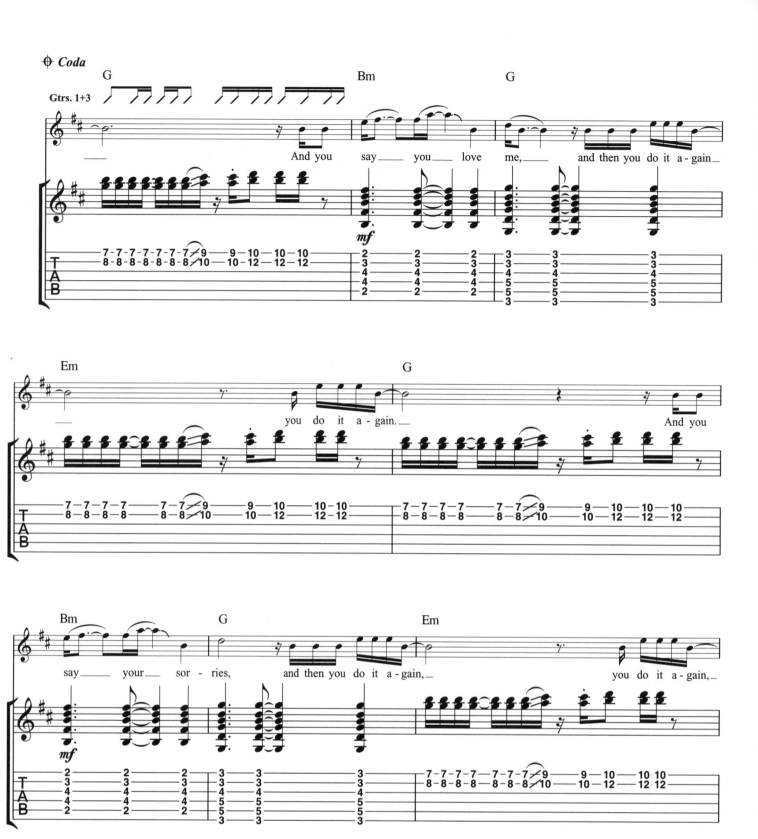

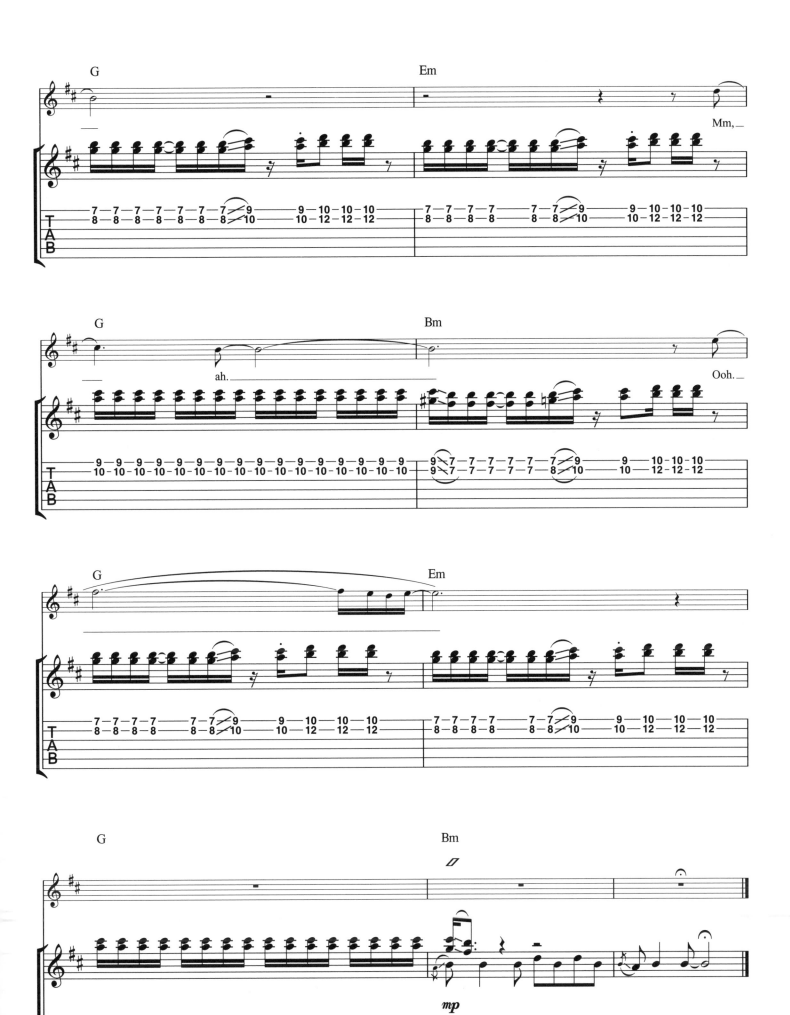

# Quicksand

Lyrics & Music by Fran Healy

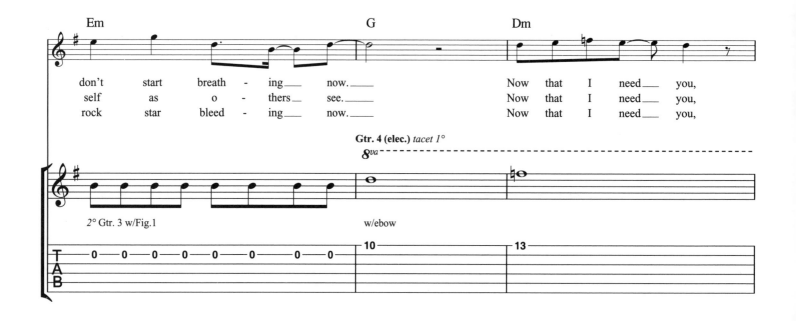

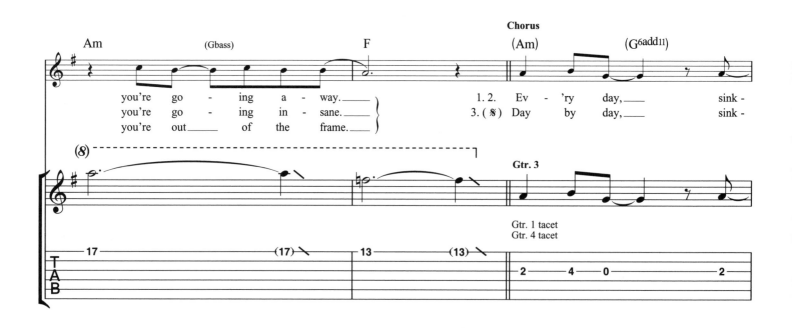

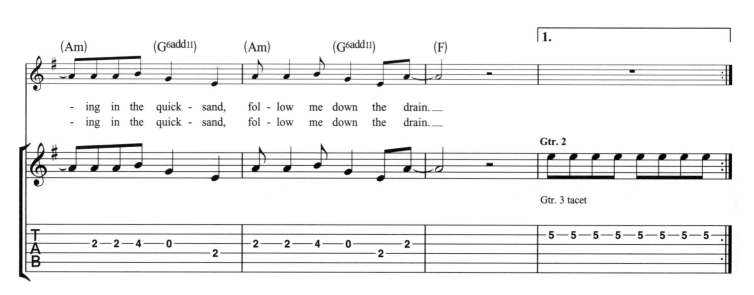

# The Beautiful Occupation

Lyrics & Music by Fran Healy

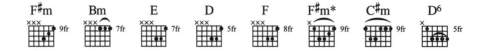

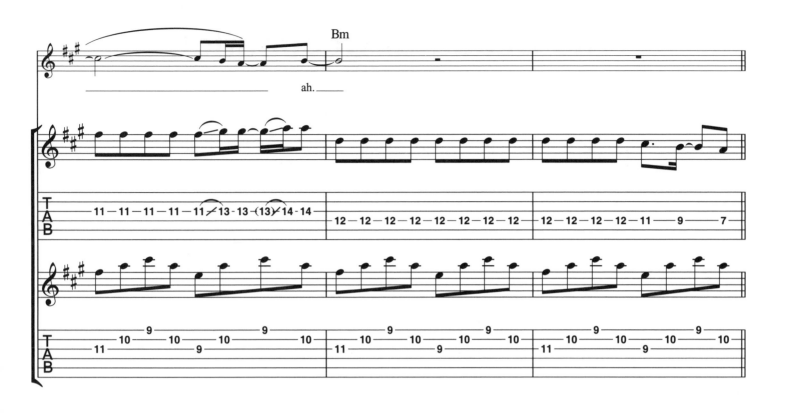

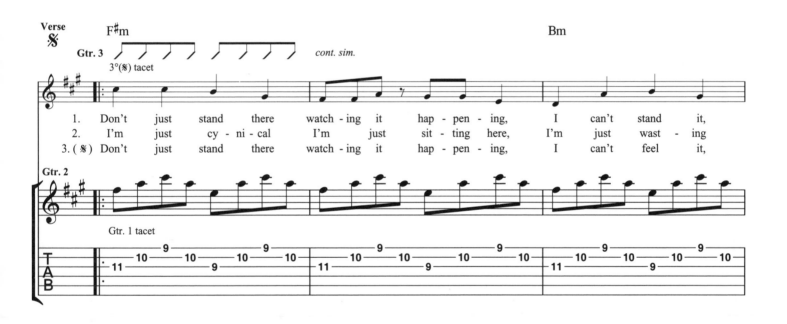

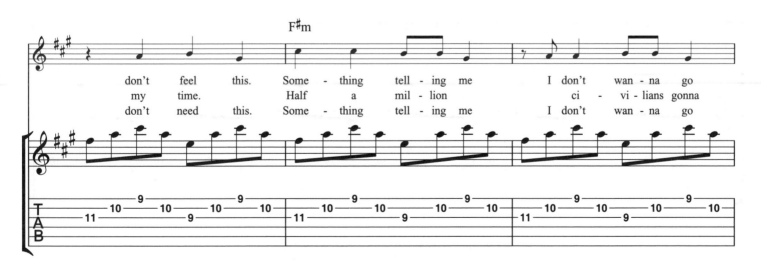

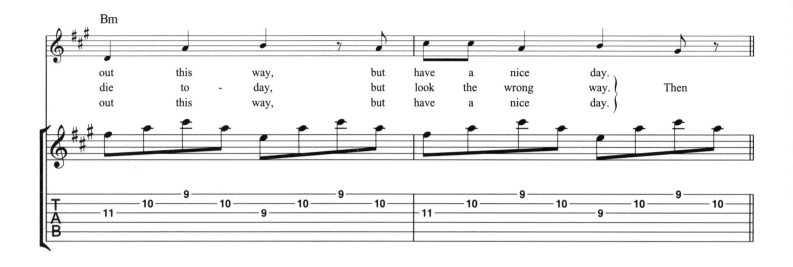

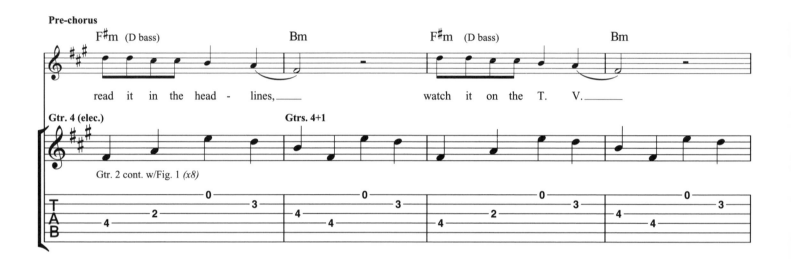

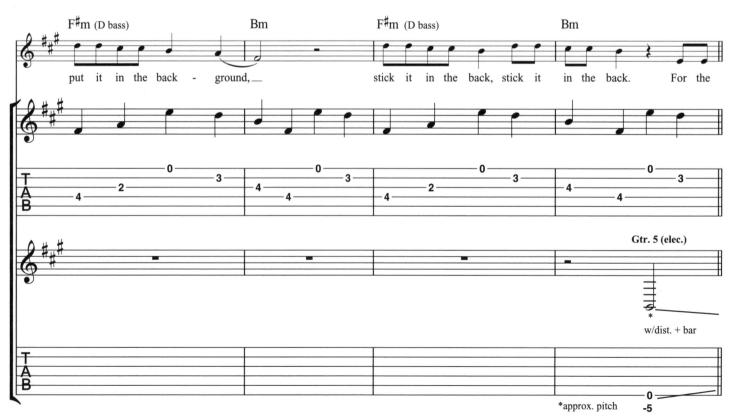

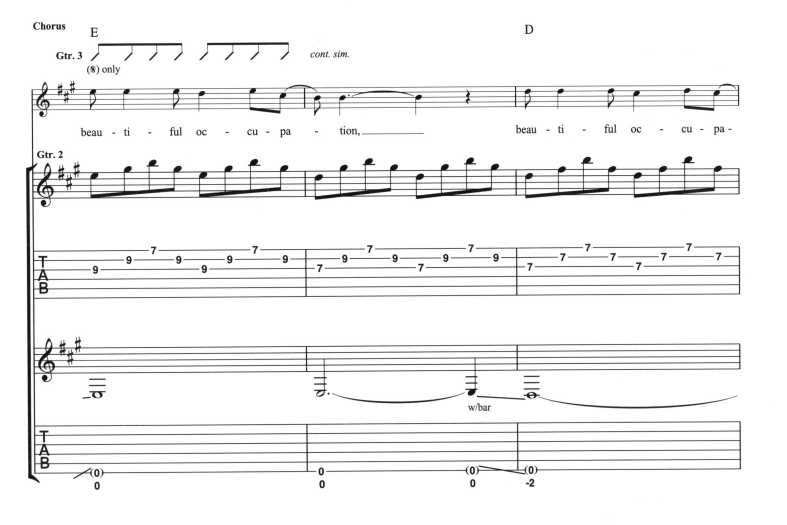

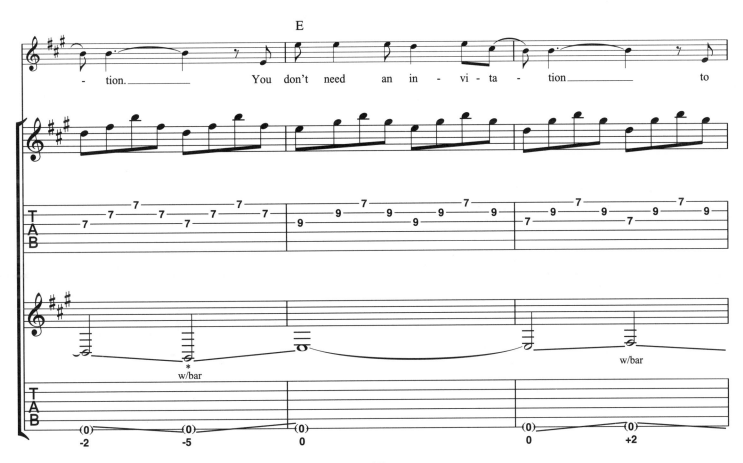

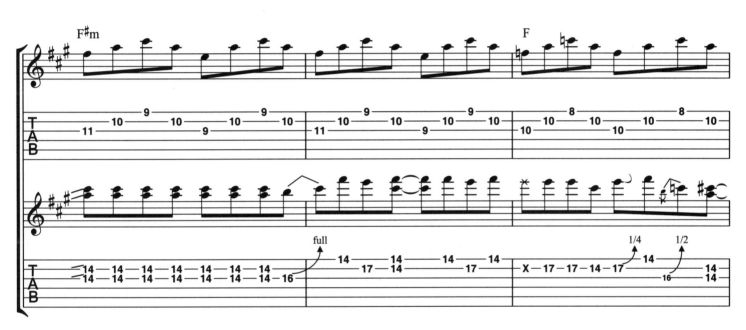

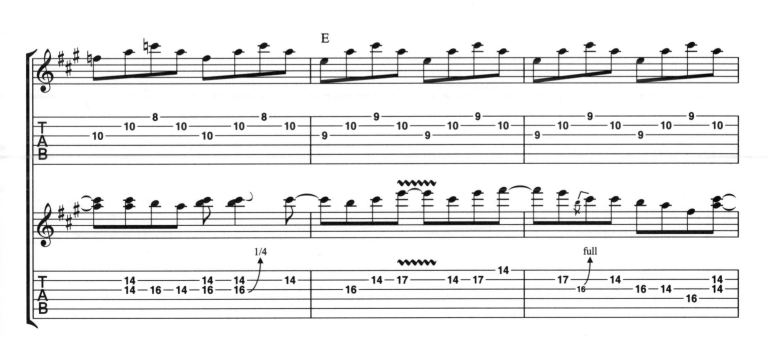

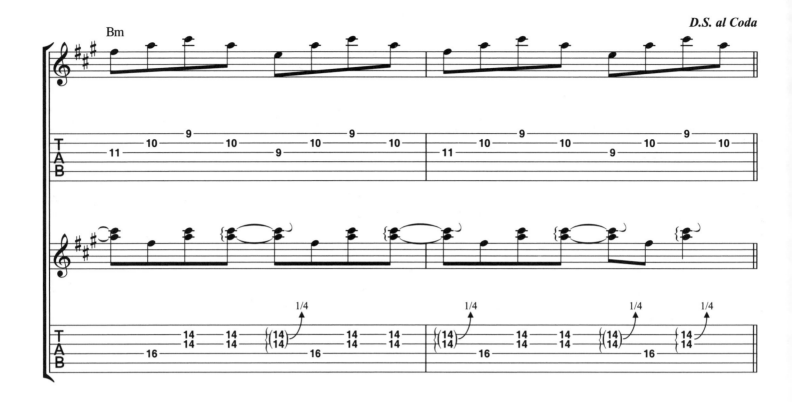

**Coda**

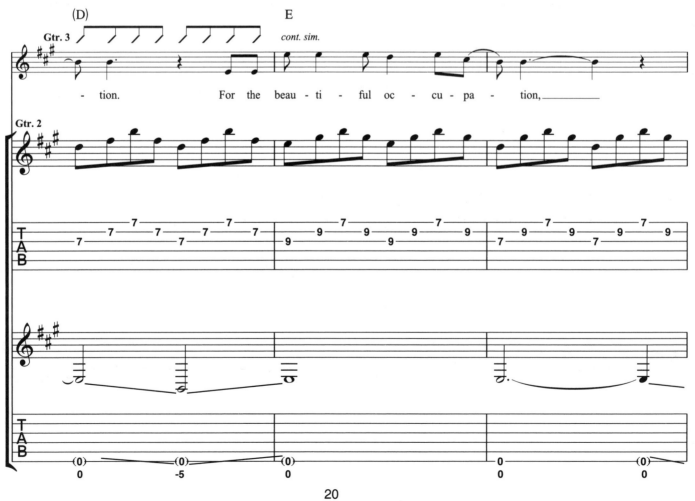

- tion.          For the beau - ti - ful oc - cu - pa - tion,_____

beau - ti - ful oc - cu - pa - tion._____ So much for an in - ter - ven - tion,_____ don't

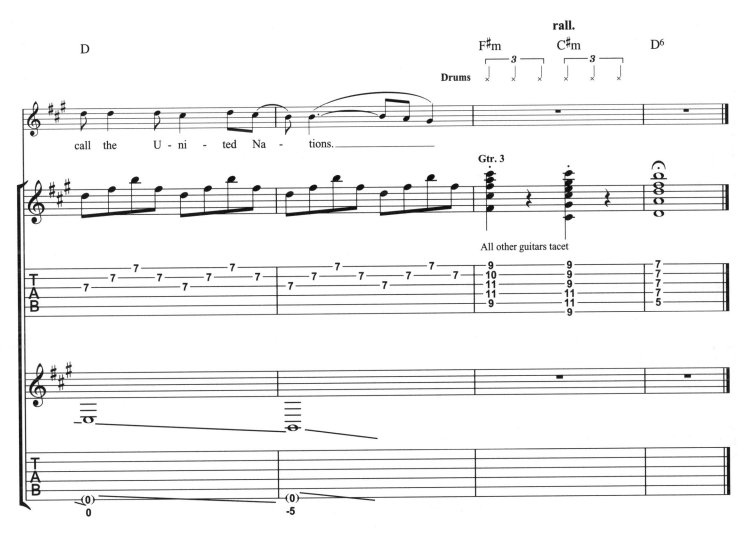

call the U - ni - ted Na - tions._____

All other guitars tacet

21

# Peace The Fuck Out

Lyrics & Music by Fran Healy

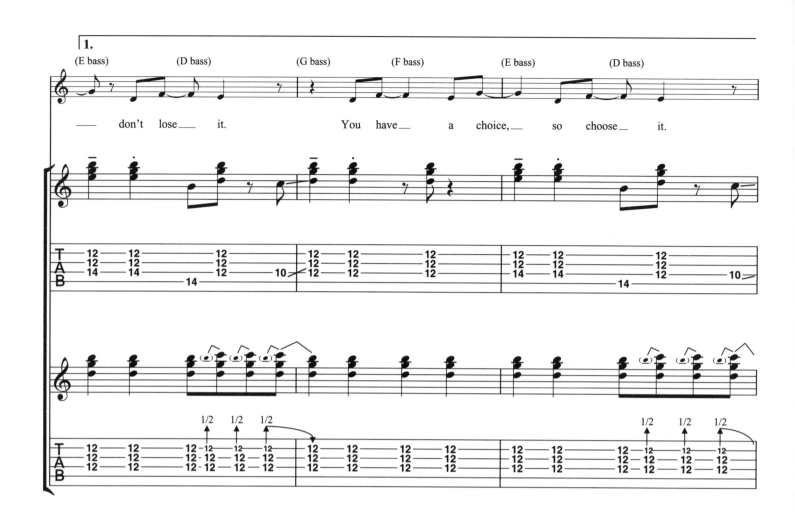

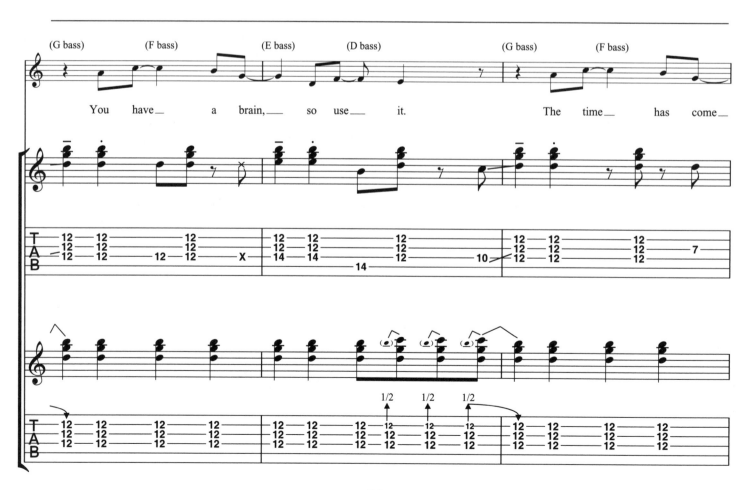

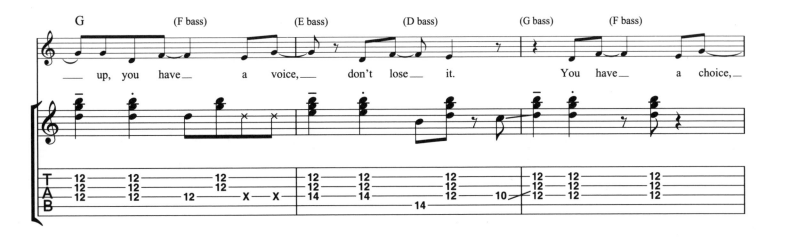

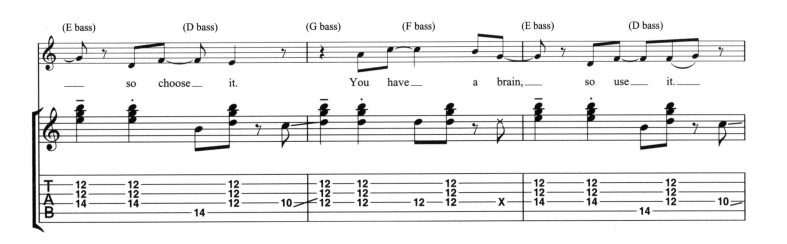

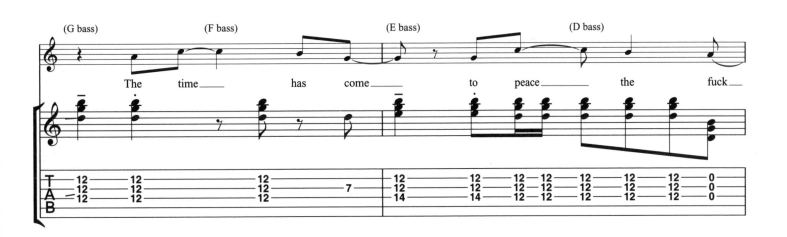

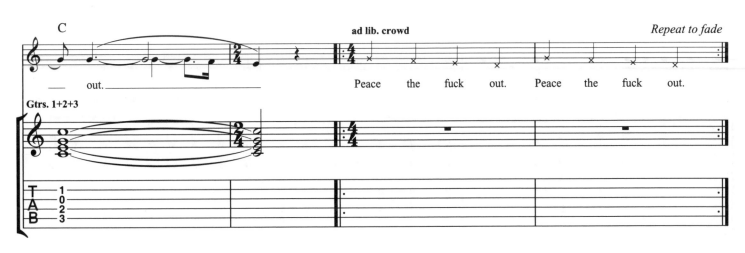

# How Many Hearts

Lyrics & Music by Fran Healy

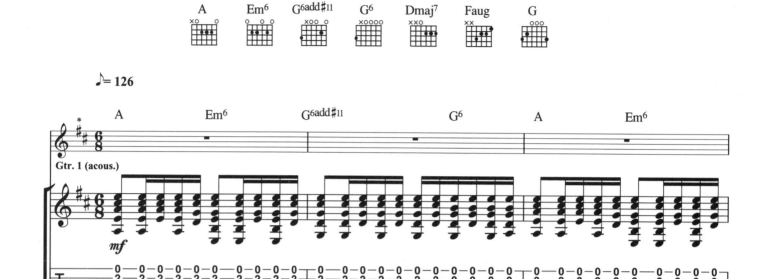

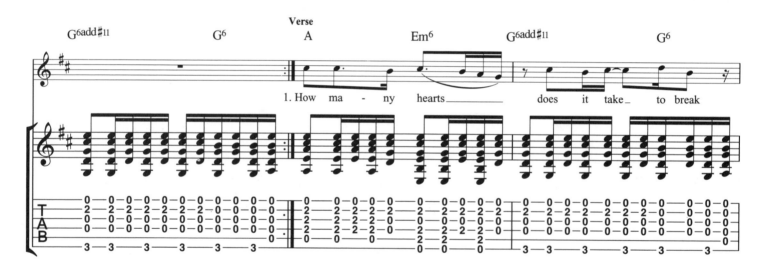

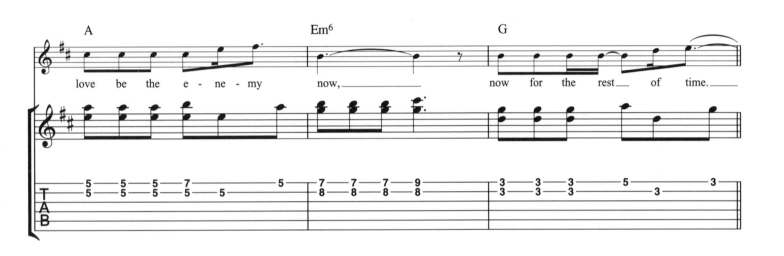

And you are and you are a new age._____

3. A

*vary volume

You are now and you are na na na._____

# Paperclips

Lyrics & Music by Fran Healy

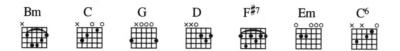

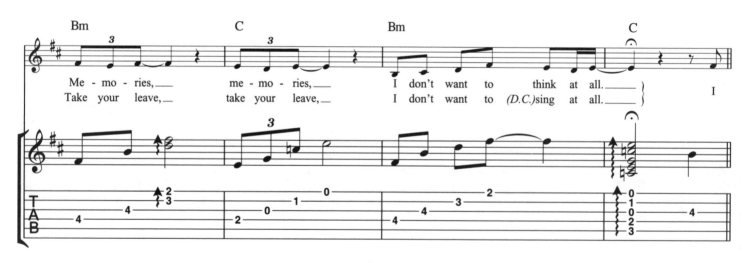

**Bridge**

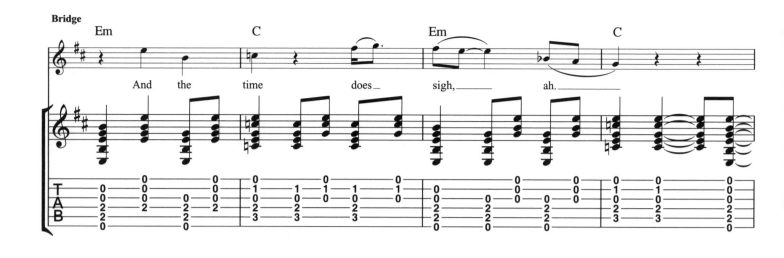

And the time does sigh, ah.

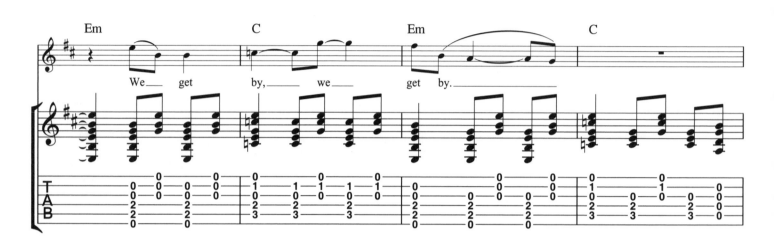

We get by, we get by.

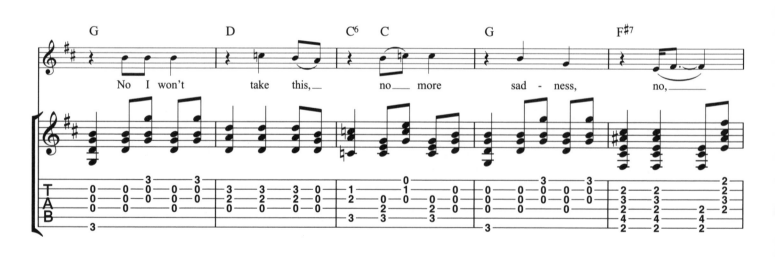

No I won't take this, no more sadness, no,

*D.C. al Coda*     ⊕ *Coda*

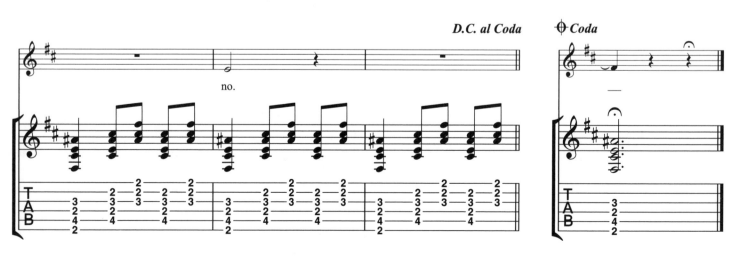

no.

36

# Somewhere Else

Lyrics & Music by Fran Healy

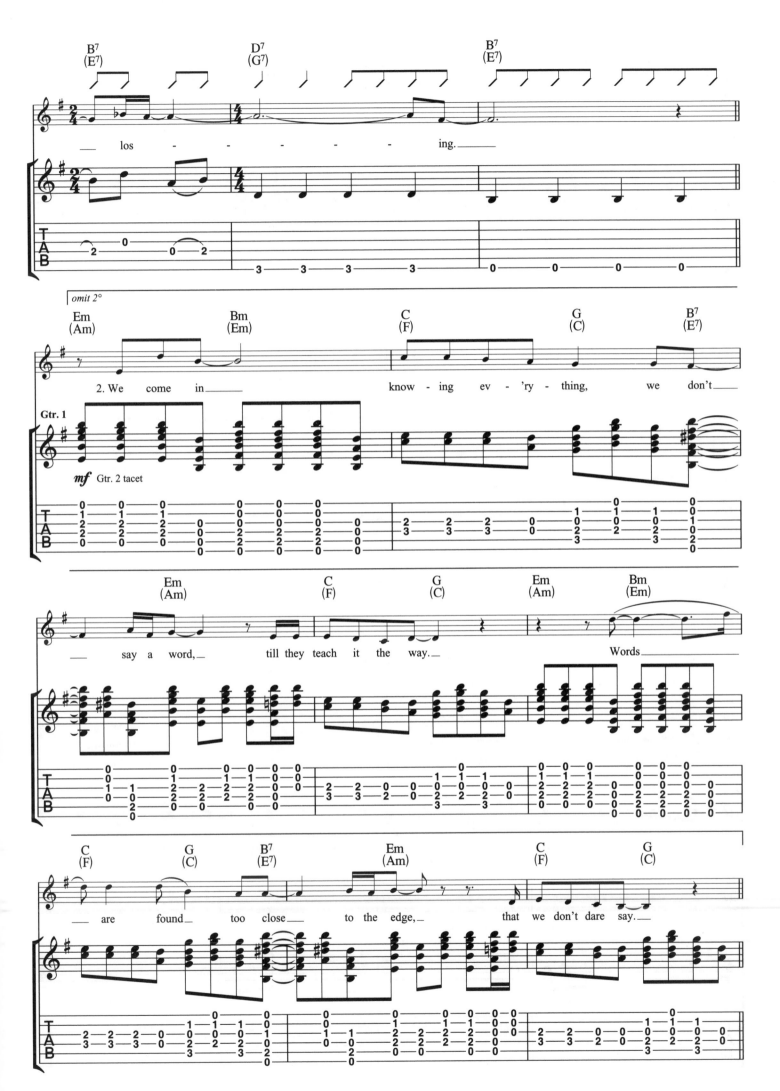

41

# Love Will Come Through

Lyrics & Music by Fran Healy

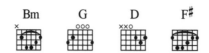

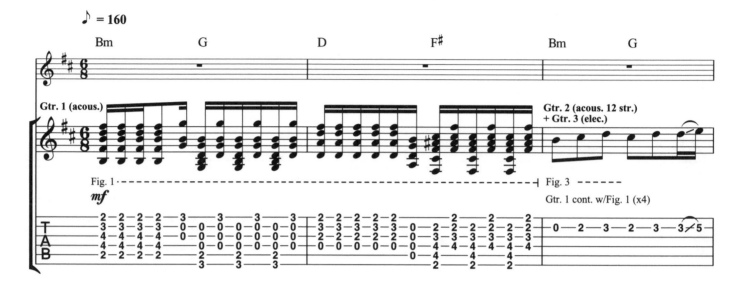

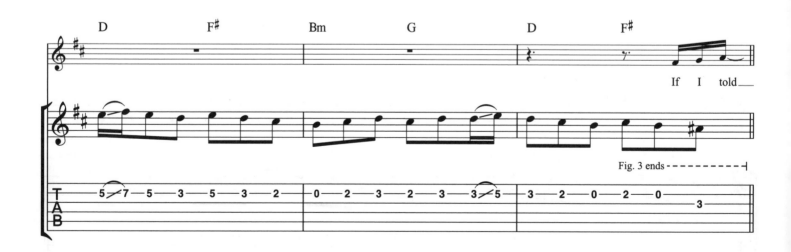

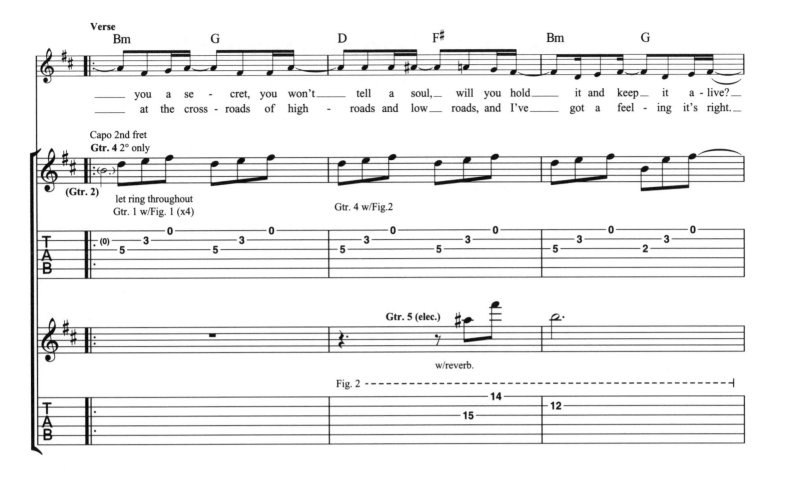

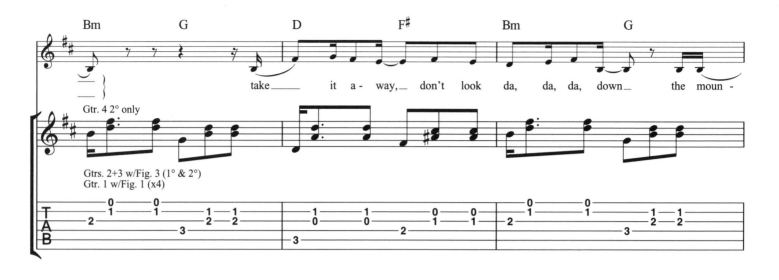

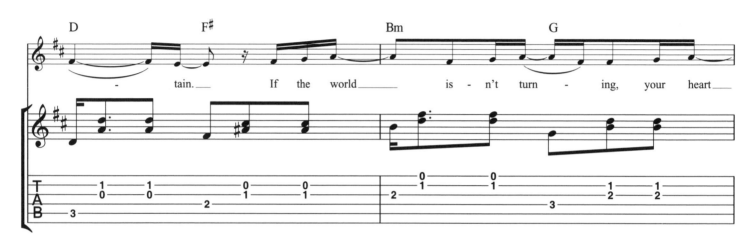

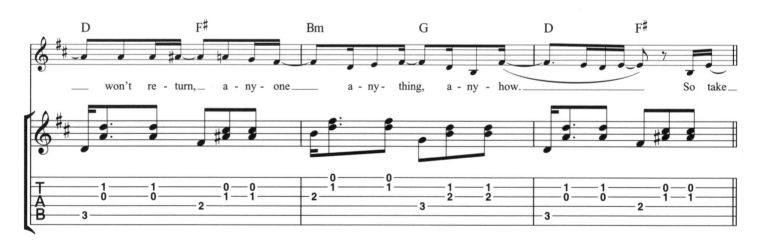

leave _____ me. Ba - by, love will come through, _____ it's just

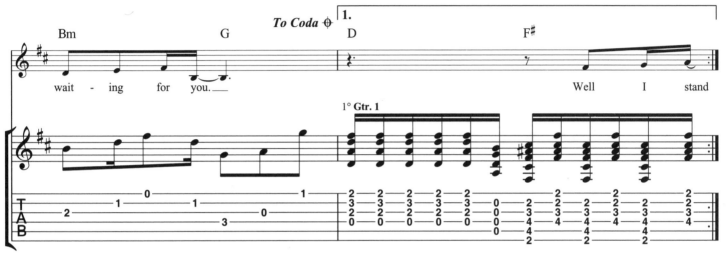

*To Coda* ⊕ **1.**

wait - ing for you. _____

Well I stand

**1° Gtr. 1**

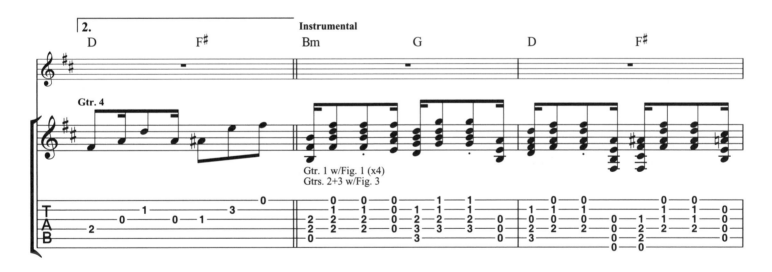

**2.**

**Instrumental**

**Gtr. 4**

Gtr. 1 w/Fig. 1 (x4)
Gtrs. 2+3 w/Fig. 3

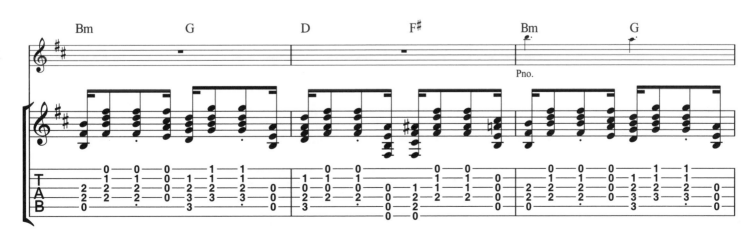

Pno.

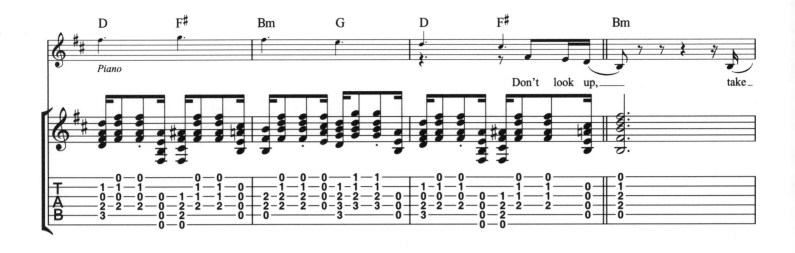

**Pre Chorus**

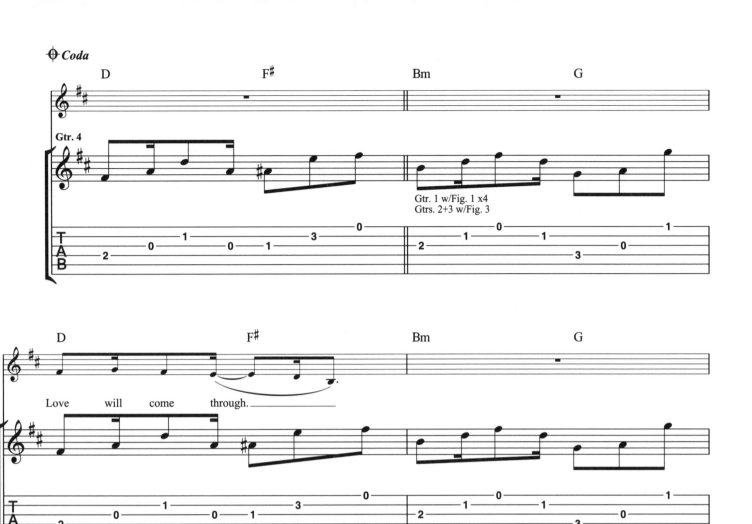

Love will come through. _____

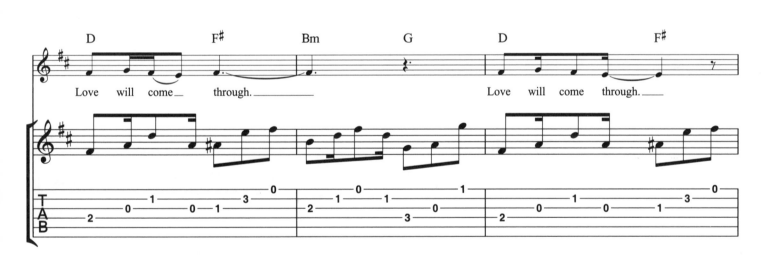

Love will come ___ through. _____      Love will come through. _____

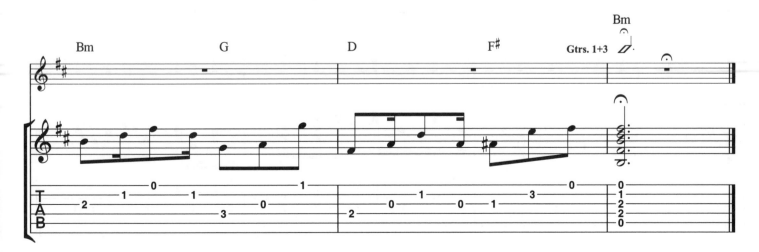

# Mid-Life Krysis

Lyrics & Music by Fran Healy

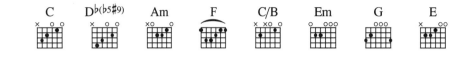

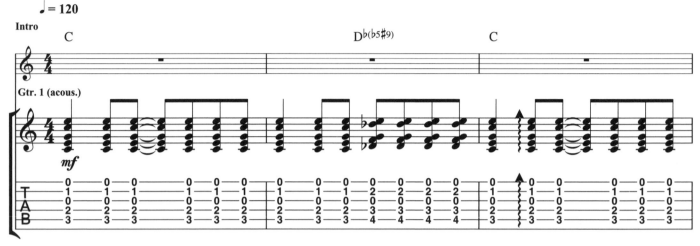

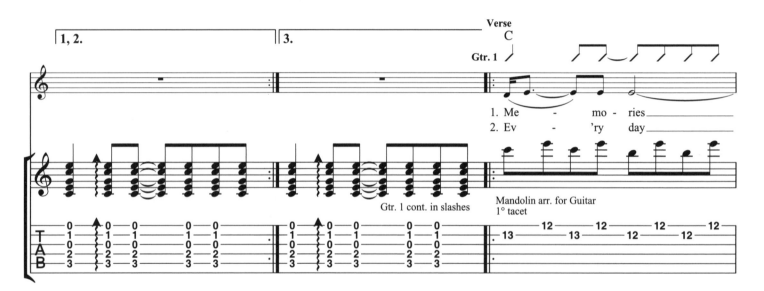

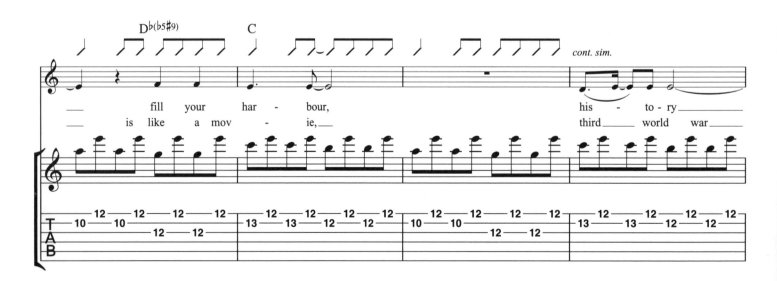

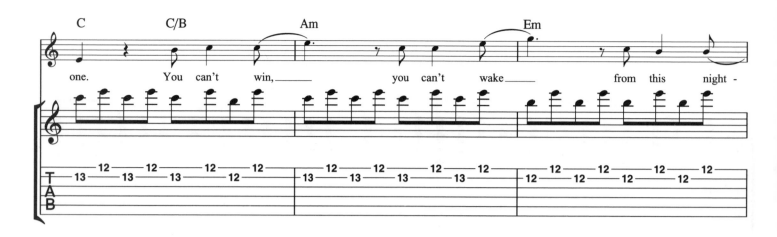

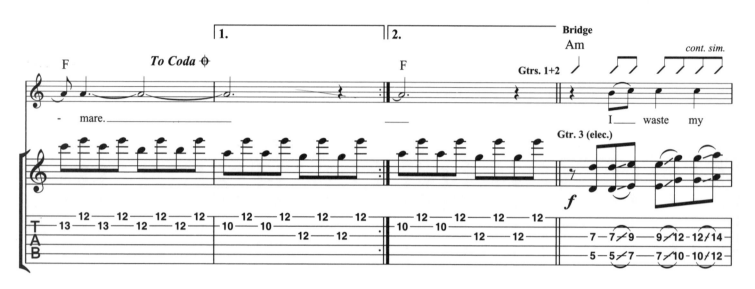

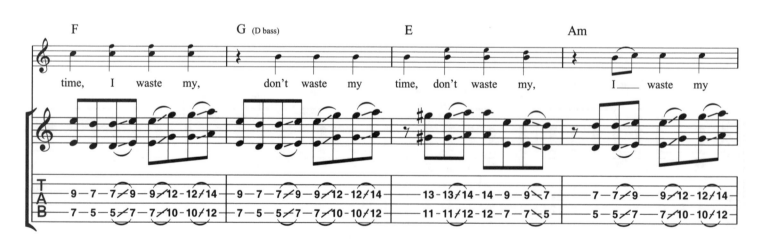

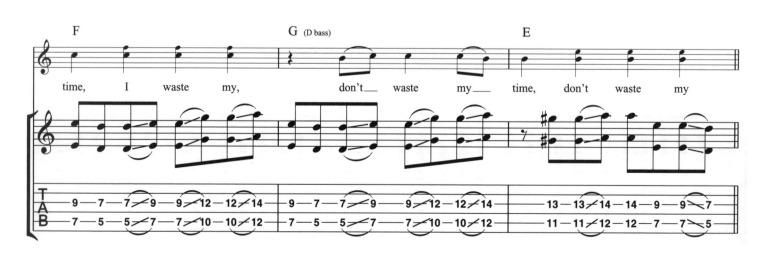

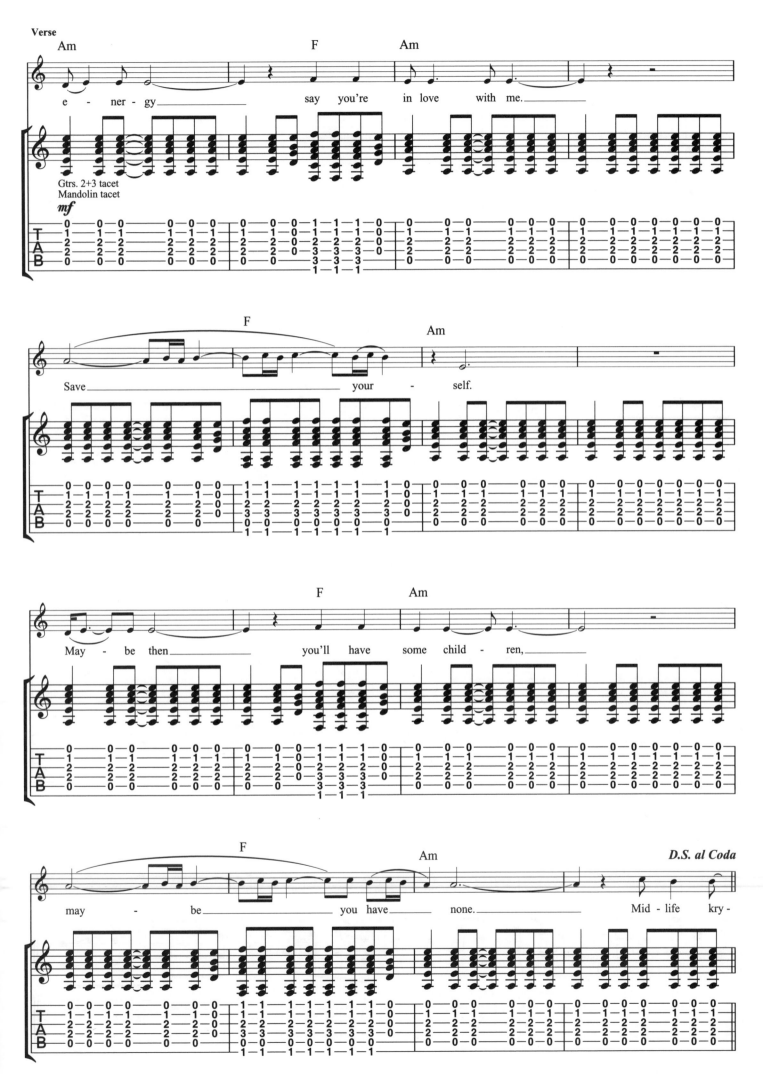

# Happy To Hang Around

### Lyrics & Music by Fran Healy

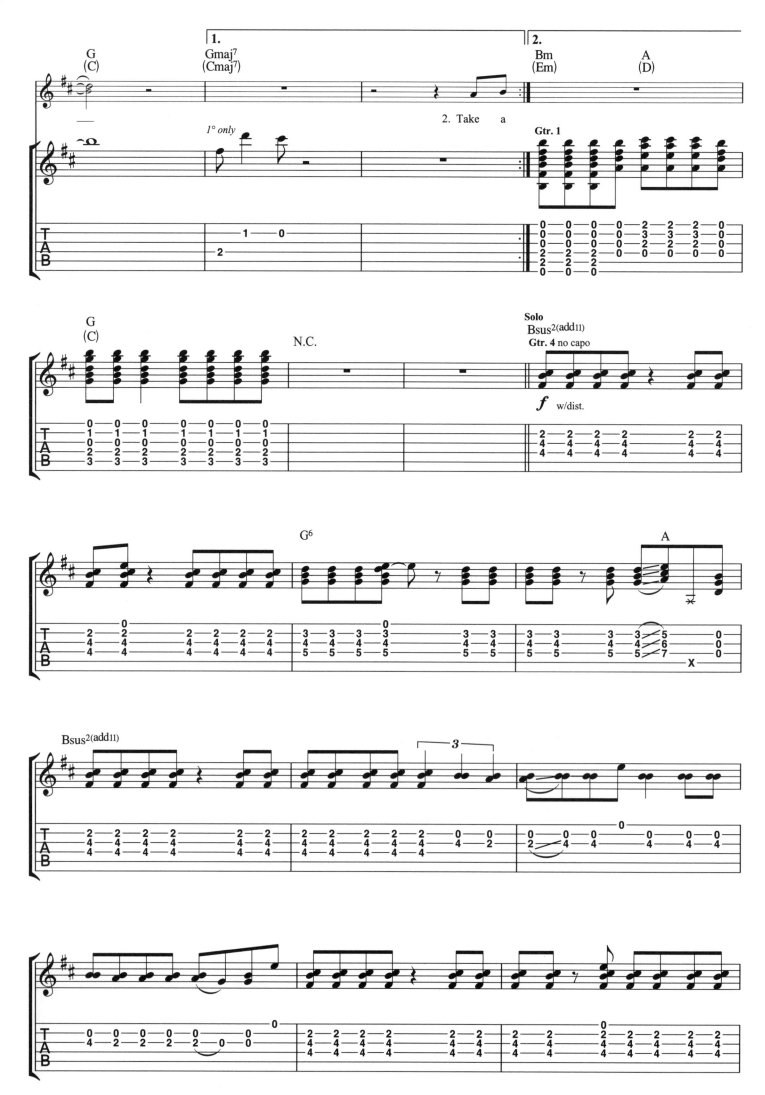

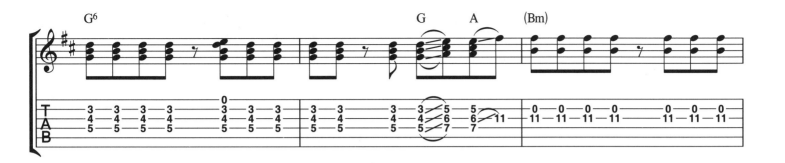

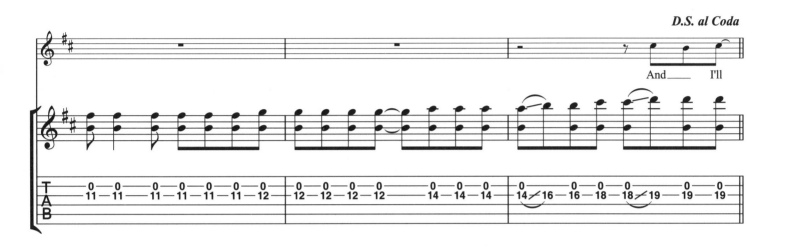

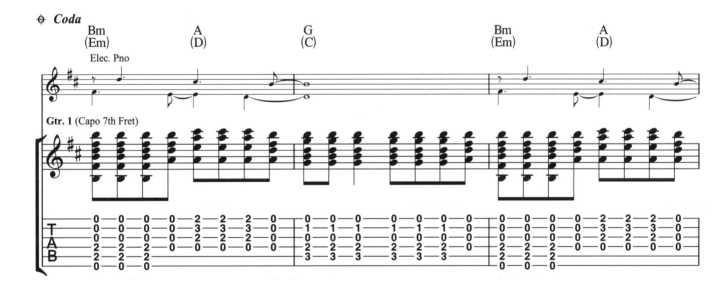

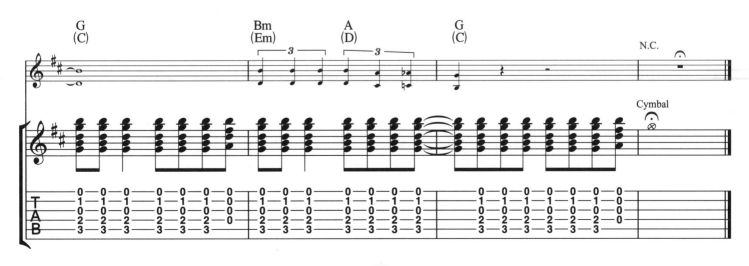

# Walking Down The Hill

Lyrics & Music by Fran Healy

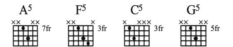

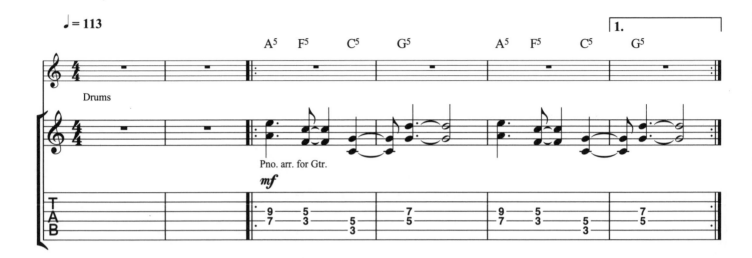

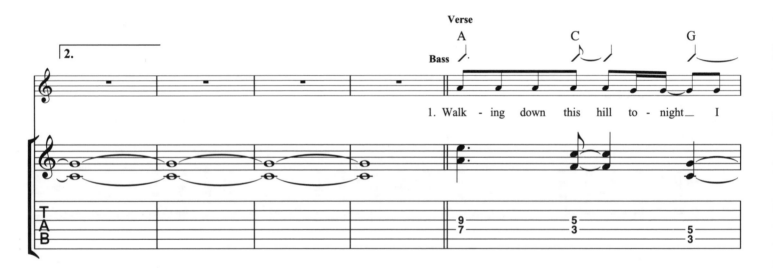

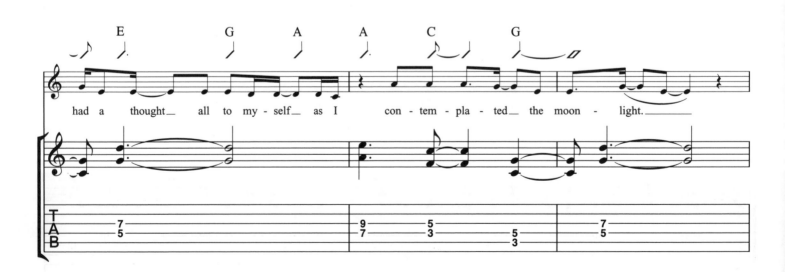

# Some Sad Song

Lyrics & Music by Fran Healy

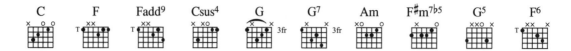

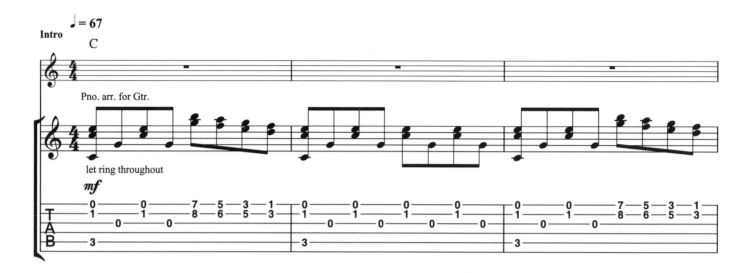

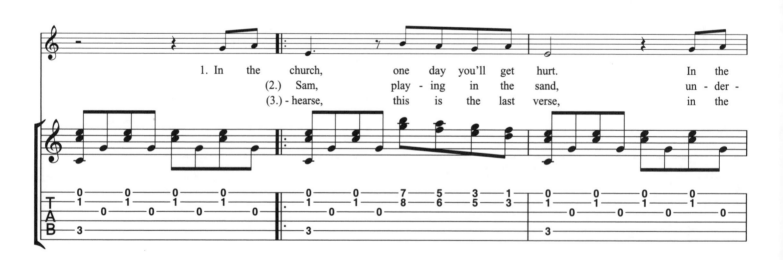

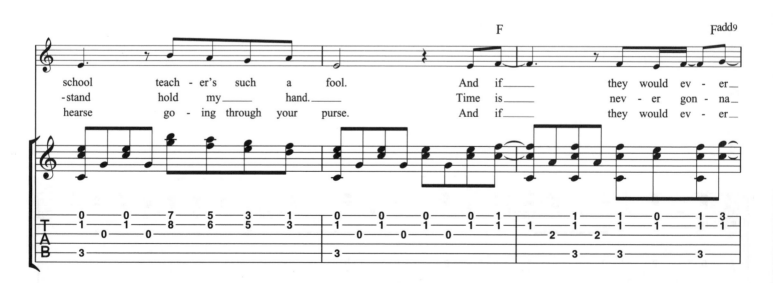

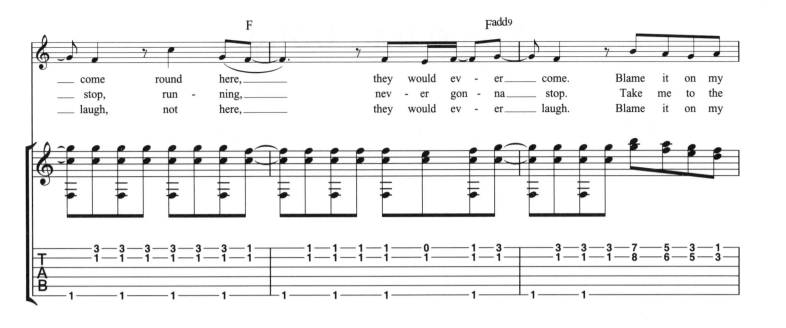

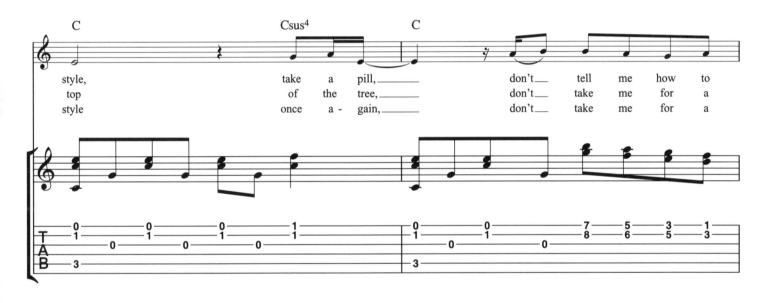

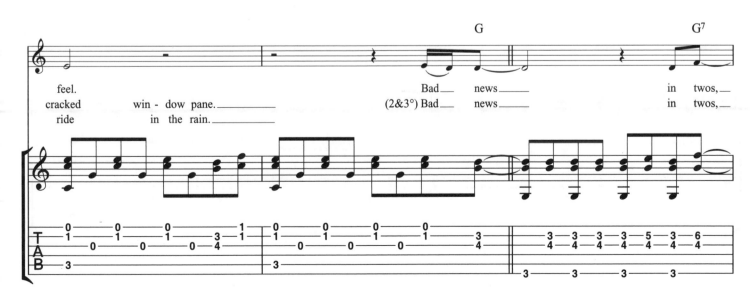